SUZIE [...]

and

AMAZING AMAZONIANS A [...]

THE SEASON FINALE

The Amazing Amazonians AFC play in Division One of the County Championships. They are having a successful season and are hoping to be promoted to the Premier Division.

OFFSIDE ALLEY TIMES

AMAZONIANS MARCHING TOGETHER

Unlike their male counterparts, the Amazonians are not well known in their local town of Pitchside Forest. They do not have much financial support but they all have other talents aside from football which they use to help their club.

Philippa Nett is the goalkeeper. She has played for a number of teams and can jump very high which compensates for her lack of height. She works in a nursery (for babies) and so is a safe pair of hands.

Gemma Flag is the right back. She is left footed which means that she can dribble very quickly down the wing and is very good at crosses. She is an accountant and makes sure that all the players pay their money (and fines!) on time.

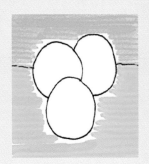

Wendy Chase is a central defender. She is very good in the air and has managed to keep a number of clean sheets. She is a PE teacher at a local school and so she takes some of the training sessions.

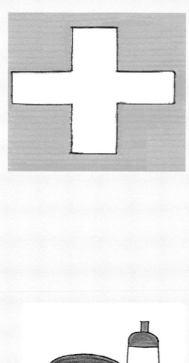

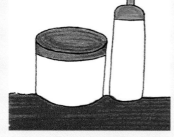

Suzie Boots is the other central defender and the captain of the Amazing Amazonians. She has played in the same team as Wendy since they were at school and together they are a formidable pair. Suzie Boots is a physiotherapist and helps her teammates if they have injuries.

Becky Shoot is the left back. She is left footed which means she can drift inside the pitch and help in midfield. She is a firewoman and her ladder has come in handy for retrieving balls after shooting practice (especially when Matilda Laces has a shot!)

Fiona Dribble is a right winger. She is well known for being able to cross the ball accurately and takes all the corners from the right. She is a plumber and was called into action when the changing rooms flooded last season.

Vicky Studs is a right midfielder. She is excellent at tackling and is not a dirty player at all. She owns a launderette and is responsible for keeping the kit clean.

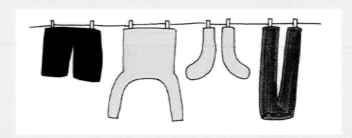

Abby Dash is the left midfielder. She is not very tall but is incredibly fast.

She has a large car which can fit in over half of the team, which is very useful for away matches.

Deidre Pass is a left winger. She complements
Abby Dash well as Deidre is not very fast but is
tall. She scores most of her goals from heading
and also takes the corners and throw-ins from
the left. She enjoys knitting and makes all the
scarves for the club's supporters.

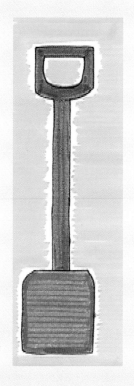

Charlie Wing is a centre forward. She is strong and is able to keep the ball well which gives time for Fiona Dribble and Deidre Pass to help her. She works in a nursery (for plants) and makes sure that the pitch is in as good a condition as possible.

Matilda Laces is the second striker. She often plays just behind Charlie Wing and is very good at chipping the ball over the opposition defenders. She owns a bakery and always makes sure that there is enough to eat for the post-match hospitality.

OFFSIDE ALLEY TIMES

AMAZONIANS MARCHING TOGETHER

Lucy Match is a sweeper but she is so good at reading the game that she can play anywhere on the pitch. She is often the substitute who comes on and makes an impact when the opposition is tiring. She is a journalist for the local paper and tries to get the Amazing Amazonians as much publicity as she can.

The Amazing Amazonians train twice a week in the evening. When it is dark, they cannot afford to turn on the floodlights and so they have to cut their training short. When this happens, the players who own cars turn on their headlights so that the players can see to change their boots.

Sometimes the Amazing Amazonians cannot afford to hire the training pitch so they train on the local park instead. When this happens, dogs often join in the training, chasing the ball. "Sign them up" jokes Rob, the coach.

Sometimes the training pitch and the park are waterlogged and the Amazing Amazonians cannot afford to hire an indoor pitch. When this happens, they have to practise heading because the water stops the ball from rolling on the ground.

The Amazing Amazonians play their matches on Sundays. Their home ground is just down Offside Alley. For away matches, they travel in convoy. Lucy Match always leads the convoy as she is the only player to have a SatNav.

Next Sunday is the most important match of the season. If they win or draw, the Amazing Amazonians will gain promotion. All of the team is very anxious. Rob is trying to work out tactics, Paul has washed his lucky socks especially, and Molly the mascot is too nervous to eat as much as she usually does.

On the day of the match, all the players meet earlier than usual at Offside Alley. As it is an away game, they are travelling in convoy but

disaster strikes when Abby's car breaks down! The match cannot start without her as she has more than half the team in her car!

Luckily Abby's husband is a mechanic. He dashes out to fix the car and gets the team moving again.

Thankfully all the team is reunited at Stadium Terrace, thirty minutes before the kick-off. After a quick warm-up and an inspirational team talk, the whistle blows for the start of the match.

The first half passes in a dreary blur. Both teams are playing defensively as neither wants to concede a goal. A draw would be enough for the Amazing Amazonians to be promoted, but Rob wants a goal.

At the start of the second half, Charlie Wing makes a break and hits a powerful shot.

The ball dips, but drifts just wide for a goal kick. Paul cheers, thinking she has scored.

Ten minutes later, the opposition win a corner.

There is some pushing in the penalty area but the
Amazonians survive. Everyone is relieved as
Philippa Nett manages to catch the ball safely.

The second half is much more open and there are equal chances for both teams.

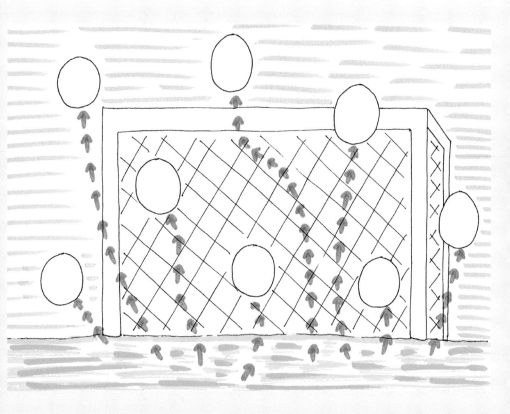

Supporters from both teams are urging their players to shoot. Molly cannot watch as she is too anxious.

Eight minutes from time, the referee blows his whistle for a penalty! Vicky Studs was fouled in the box and Matilda Laces puts the ball on the spot.

A hush descends around Stadium Terrace. Matilda takes two steps back and strikes the ball.

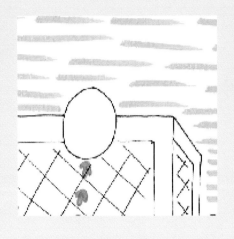

Molly howls as the ball sails high over the bar.

Paul touches his lucky socks. He can barely watch he is so nervous. Just one goal would be enough but the Amazing Amazonians have to do some defending before the final whistle blows.

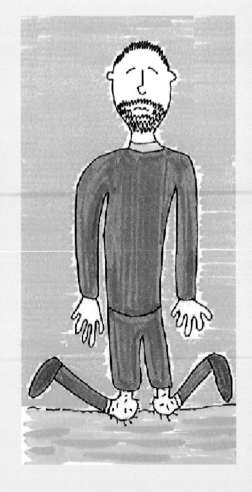

The Amazing Amazonians do not have long to go.

In the remaining minutes, Becky Shoot, Deidre Pass and Captain Suzie Boots make some excellent tackles to deny shooting opportunities.

All eyes are on the referee. He puts the whistle to his lips but takes an age to blow. Supporters of the Amazing Amazonians are really nervous.

Eventually the whistle sounds and pierces the tension. The Amazing Amazonians have done enough to be promoted! They are wild with joy!

Suzie Boots is awarded the trophy on behalf of her team. Next season the Amazing Amazonians will be playing in the Premier Division.

They have just signed a new player, Sophie Chip who is a carpenter and has made the cabinet for the trophy and the frame for the team photo which will hang in the clubhouse.